Memories of
My Baptism

PUT
YOUR
PICTURE
HERE!

Memories of

My Baptism

Printed in The United States
First Printing: February 1998

16 15 14 13 12 11   18 17 16 15 14 13 12

ISBN 13: 978-1-57734-271-7 (boy)

ISBN 13: 978-1-57734-237-3 (girl)

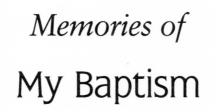

Memories of

My Baptism

*Except a man be born of water and of the Spirit, he
cannot enter into the kingdom of God.*
(John 3:5)

Covenant Communications, Inc.

The Baptism Journal

of

Then cometh Jesus from Galilee to Jordan unto John, to be baptized of him. (Matthew 3:13)

We believe that the first principles and ordinances of the Gospel are: first, Faith in the Lord Jesus Christ; second, Repentance; third, Baptism by immersion for the remission of sins; fourth, Laying on of hands for the gift of the Holy Ghost (Fourth Article of Faith)

I know when I am baptized my wrongs are washed away,
And I can be forgiven and improve myself each day.
I want my life to be as clean as earth right after rain
I want to be the best I can and live with God again.

("When I Am Baptized" *Children's Songbook*, words and music by Nita
Dale Milner, p. 103)

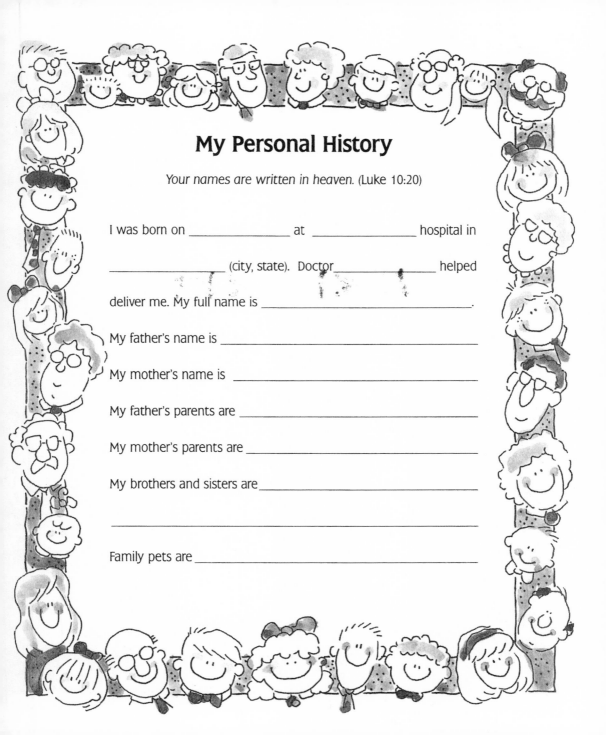

My Personal History

Your names are written in heaven. (Luke 10:20)

I was born on _____ at _____ hospital in

_____ (city, state). Doctor_____ helped

deliver me. My full name is _____.

My father's name is _____

My mother's name is _____

My father's parents are _____

My mother's parents are _____

My brothers and sisters are_____

_____

Family pets are _____

On _____ (date) I was given a name and a blessing

by _____ who holds the office of

_____ (priesthood). These were

some of the special promises given during my blessing:

_____

_____

I was _____ days old when I received this blessing.

My bishop was _____. My family lived in

the _____ Ward. The Prophet and President of the Church

was _____.

Place baby picture here.

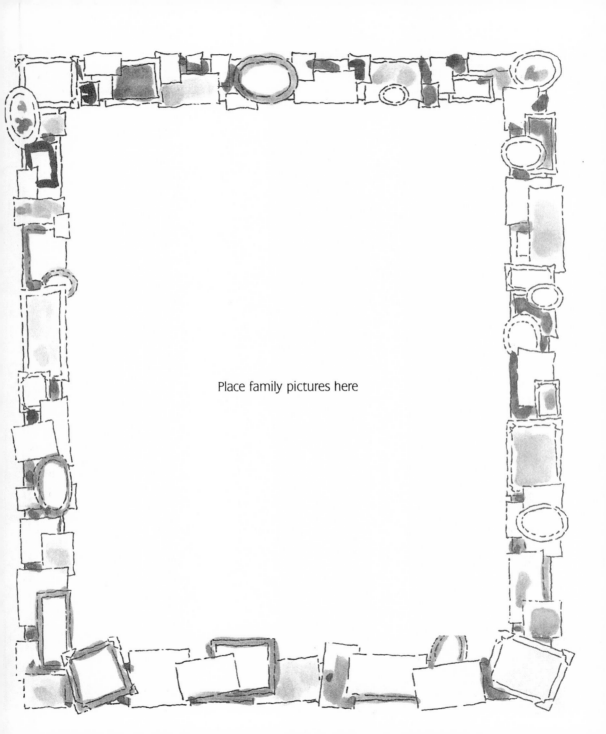

Place family pictures here

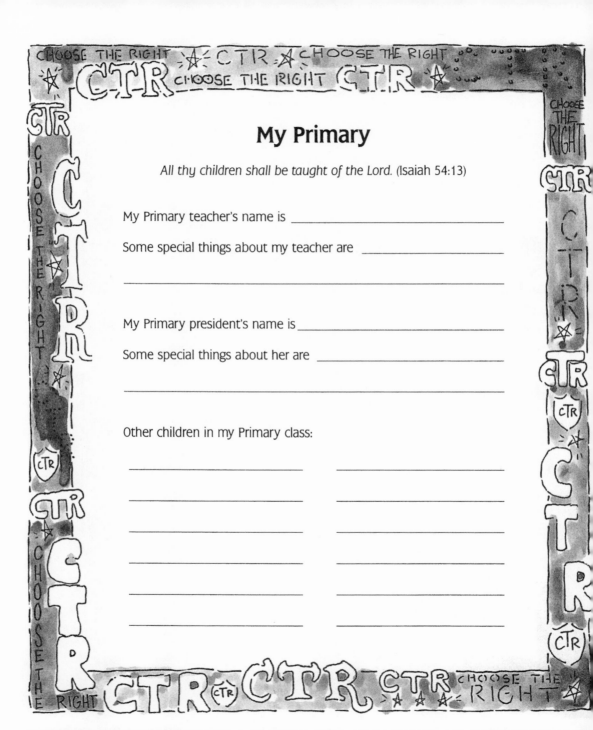

My Primary

All thy children shall be taught of the Lord. (Isaiah 54:13)

My Primary teacher's name is _____

Some special things about my teacher are _____

_____

My Primary president's name is _____

Some special things about her are _____

_____

Other children in my Primary class:

_____   _____

_____   _____

_____   _____

_____   _____

_____   _____

_____

My favorite Primary songs are:

_____

_____

_____

The things I like best about Primary are:

_____

_____

_____

My best friends at Primary are:

_____

_____

_____

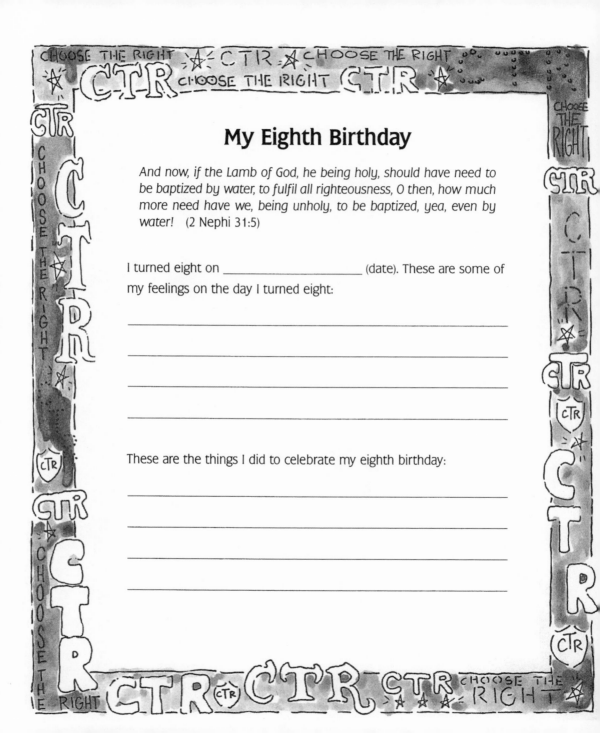

My Eighth Birthday

And now, if the Lamb of God, he being holy, should have need to be baptized by water, to fulfil all righteousness, O then, how much more need have we, being unholy, to be baptized, yea, even by water! (2 Nephi 31:5)

I turned eight on _____ (date). These are some of my feelings on the day I turned eight:

_____

_____

_____

_____

These are the things I did to celebrate my eighth birthday:

_____

_____

_____

_____

These are the things I did to prepare for my baptism:

_____

_____

_____

These are the things my parents did to help me prepare for my baptism:

_____

_____

_____

Bishop _____ (name) interviewed me

on _____ (date) at _____ (place).

One thing he said that I especially remember is

_____

_____

_____

_____

Baptism is to be administered in the following manner unto all those who repent–

The person who is called of God and has authority from Jesus Christ to baptize, shall go down into the water with the person who has presented himself or herself for baptism, and shall say, calling him or her by name: Having been commissioned of Jesus Christ, I baptize you in the name of the Father, and of the Son, and of the Holy Ghost.

Then shall he immerse him or her in the water, and come forth again out of the water.

(D&C 20:72-74)

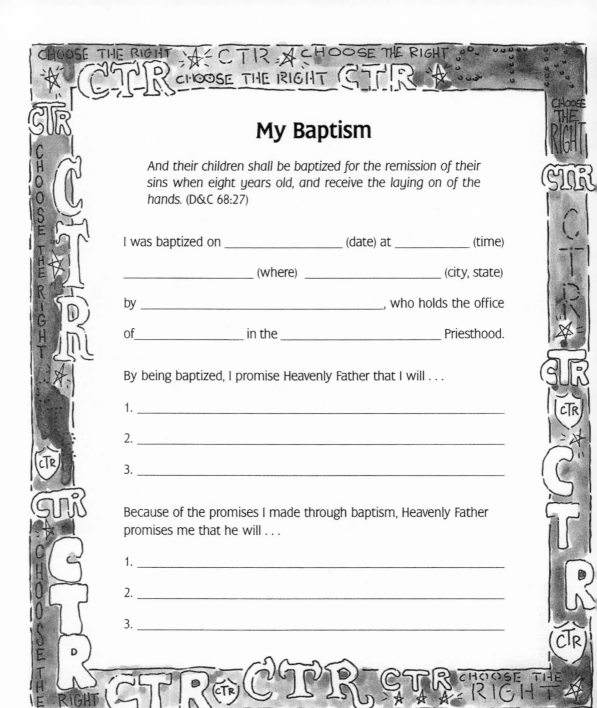

My Baptism

And their children shall be baptized for the remission of their sins when eight years old, and receive the laying on of the hands. (D&C 68:27)

I was baptized on _____ (date) at _____ (time)

_____ (where) _____ (city, state)

by _____, who holds the office

of _____ in the _____ Priesthood.

By being baptized, I promise Heavenly Father that I will . . .

1. _____

2. _____

3. _____

Because of the promises I made through baptism, Heavenly Father promises me that he will . . .

1. _____

2. _____

3. _____

These are some of my feelings on the day I was baptized:

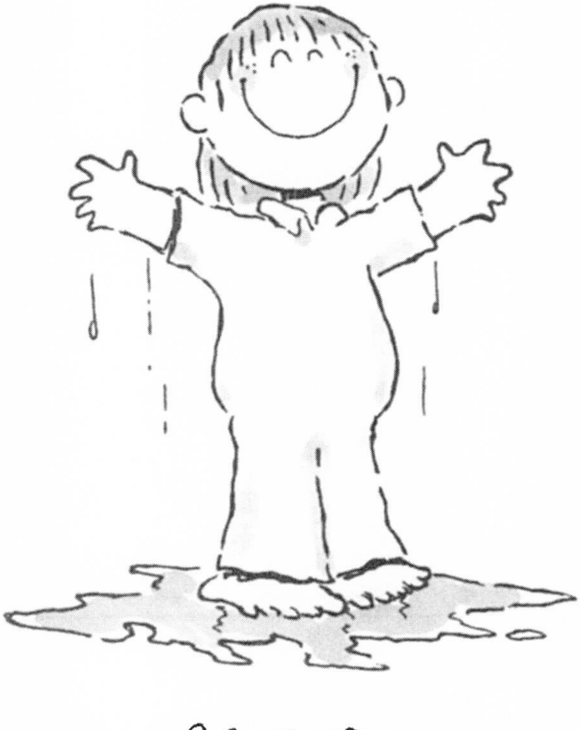

My Baptismal Program

The opening prayer was given by: _____

Talks were given by: _____

_____

_____

Musical numbers performed: _____

_____

_____

The closing prayer was given by: _____

What I especially remember about the program:

_____

_____

_____

_____

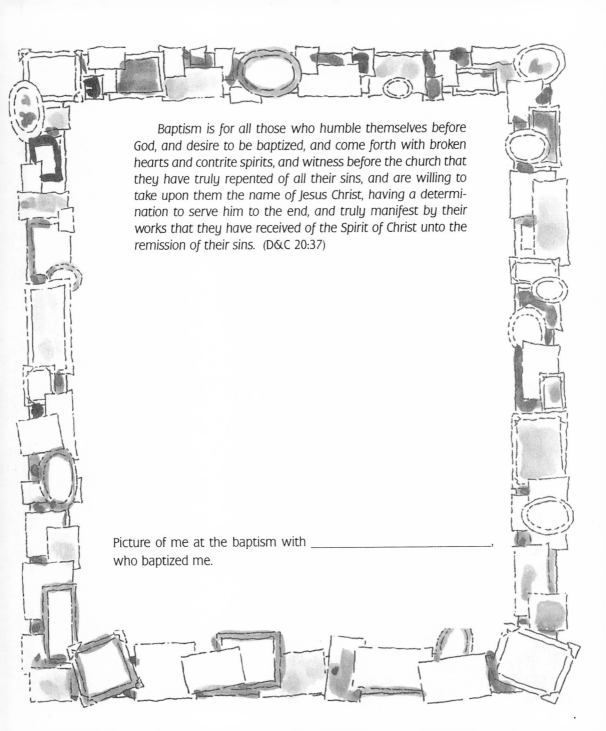

Baptism is for all those who humble themselves before God, and desire to be baptized, and come forth with broken hearts and contrite spirits, and witness before the church that they have truly repented of all their sins, and are willing to take upon them the name of Jesus Christ, having a determination to serve him to the end, and truly manifest by their works that they have received of the Spirit of Christ unto the remission of their sins. (D&C 20:37)

Picture of me at the baptism with _____,
who baptized me.

My Confirmation

He that is baptized in my name, to him will the Father give the Holy Ghost, like unto me. (2 Nephi 31:12)

I was confirmed on _____ (date) at _____ (place)

by _____, who holds the office of _____.

These are some of my feelings on the day I was confirmed:

_____

_____

_____

_____

These are some of the reasons I am glad to have the Holy Ghost:

_____

_____

_____

_____

Repent, and be baptized every one of you in the name of Jesus Christ for the remission of sins, and ye shall receive the gift of the Holy Ghost. (Acts 2:38)

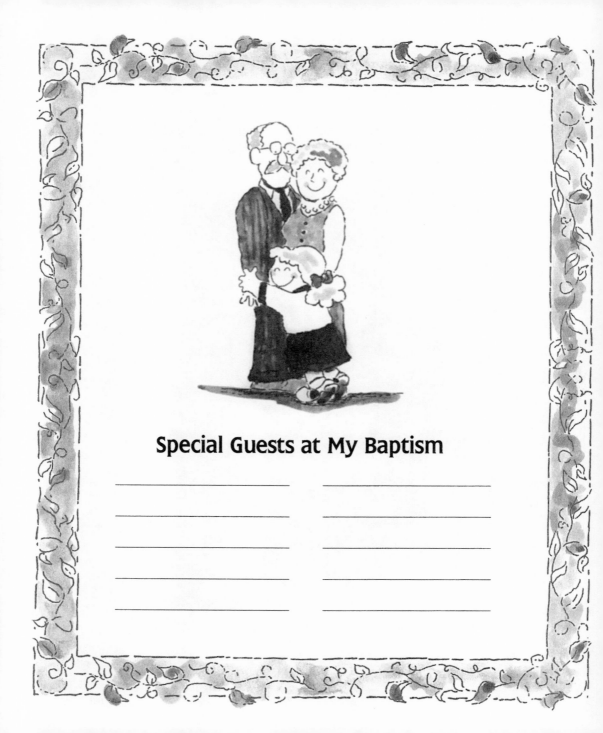

Special Guests at My Baptism

_____   _____

_____   _____

_____   _____

_____   _____

_____   _____

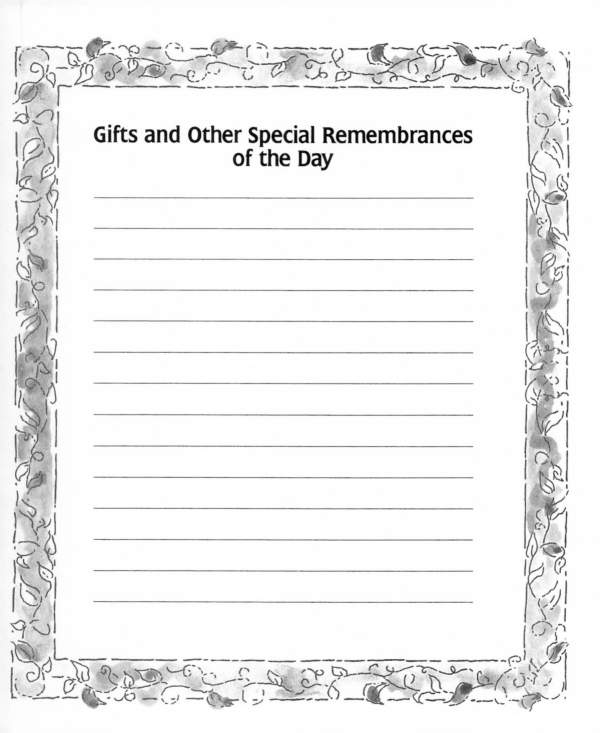

Gifts and Other Special Remembrances
of the Day

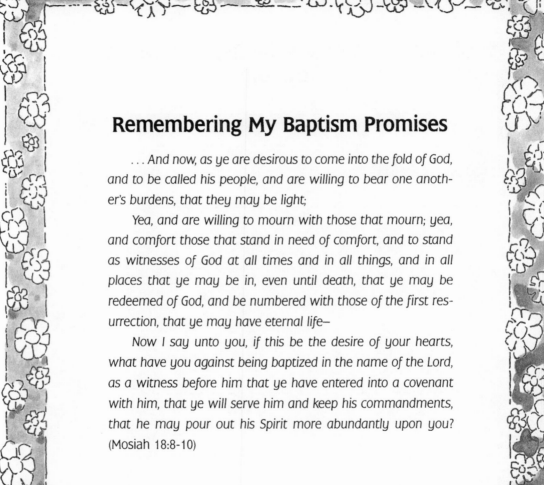

Remembering My Baptism Promises

... And now, as ye are desirous to come into the fold of God, and to be called his people, and are willing to bear one another's burdens, that they may be light;

Yea, and are willing to mourn with those that mourn; yea, and comfort those that stand in need of comfort, and to stand as witnesses of God at all times and in all things, and in all places that ye may be in, even until death, that ye may be redeemed of God, and be numbered with those of the first resurrection, that ye may have eternal life–

Now I say unto you, if this be the desire of your hearts, what have you against being baptized in the name of the Lord, as a witness before him that ye have entered into a covenant with him, that ye will serve him and keep his commandments, that he may pour out his Spirit more abundantly upon you? (Mosiah 18:8-10)

I will take the sacrament to remember these promises I made when I was baptized. During the sacrament, I will think about:

_____

_____

_____

_____

_____

Prayer upon the Bread

O God, the Eternal Father, we ask thee in the name of thy Son, Jesus Christ, to bless and sanctify this bread to the souls of all those who partake of it, that they may eat in remembrance of the body of thy Son, and witness unto thee, O God, the Eternal Father, that they are willing to take upon them the name of thy Son, and always remember him and keep his commandments which he has given them; that they may always have his Spirit to be with them. Amen. (D&C 20:77)

Prayer upon the Water

O God, the Eternal Father, we ask thee in the name of thy Son, Jesus Christ, to bless and sanctify this [water] to the souls of all those who drink of it, that they may do it in remembrance of the blood of thy Son, which was shed for them, that they may witness unto thee, O God the Eternal Father, that they do always remember him, that they may have his Spirit to be with them. Amen. (D&C 20:79)

My Testimony

_____

_____

_____

_____

_____

_____

_____

_____

_____

_____

_____

_____

_____

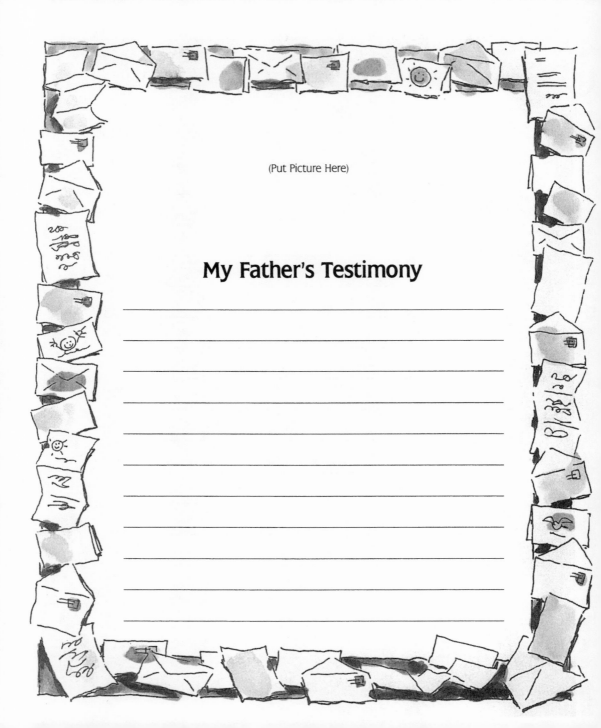

(Put Picture Here)

My Father's Testimony

_____

_____

_____

_____

_____

_____

_____

_____

_____

_____

_____

(Put Picture Here)

My Mother's Testimony

My Bishop's Testimony

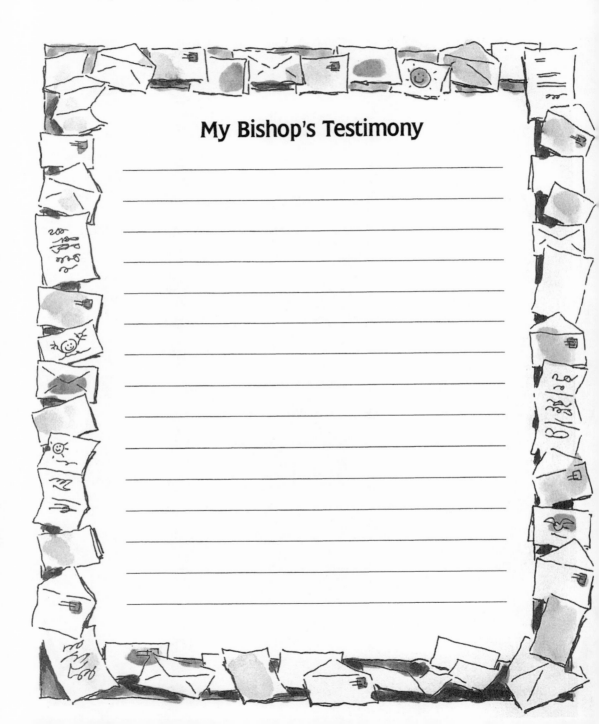

My Primary Teacher's Testimony

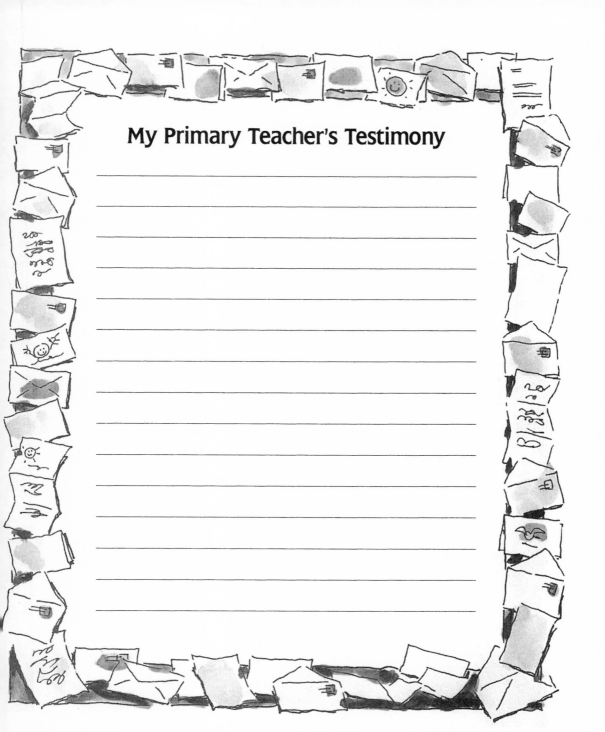

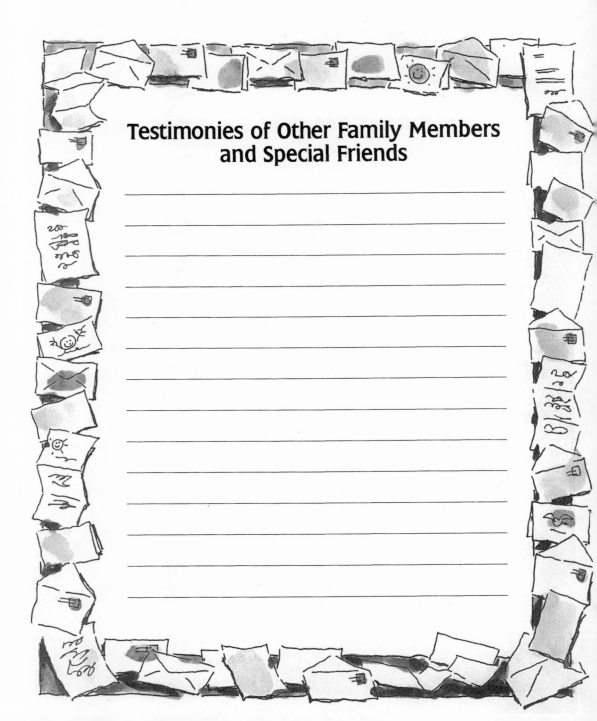

Testimonies of Other Family Members and Special Friends

_____

_____

_____

_____

_____

_____

_____

_____

_____

_____

_____

_____

_____

_____

_____

Testimonies of Other Family Members and Special Friends

_____

_____

_____

_____

_____

_____

_____

_____

_____

_____

_____

_____

_____

_____

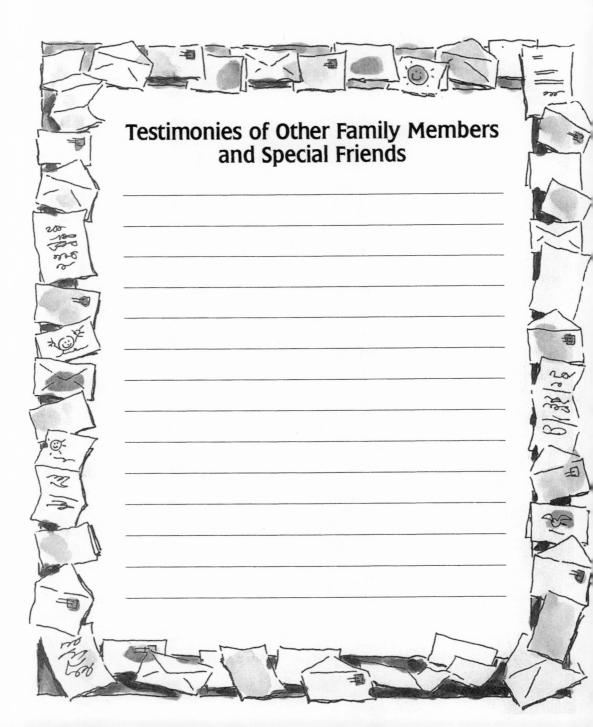

Testimonies of Other Family Members and Special Friends

Testimonies of Other Family Members and Special Friends

_____

_____

_____

_____

_____

_____

_____

_____

_____

_____

_____

_____

_____

_____

_____

_____

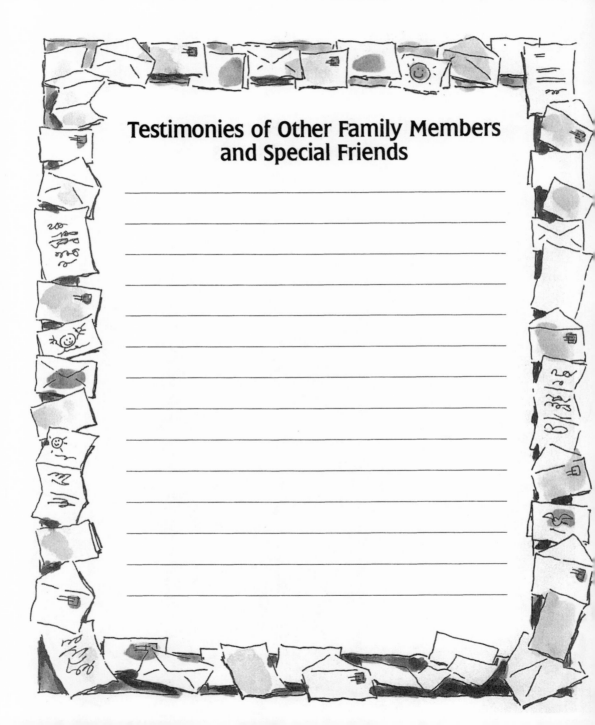

Testimonies of Other Family Members and Special Friends

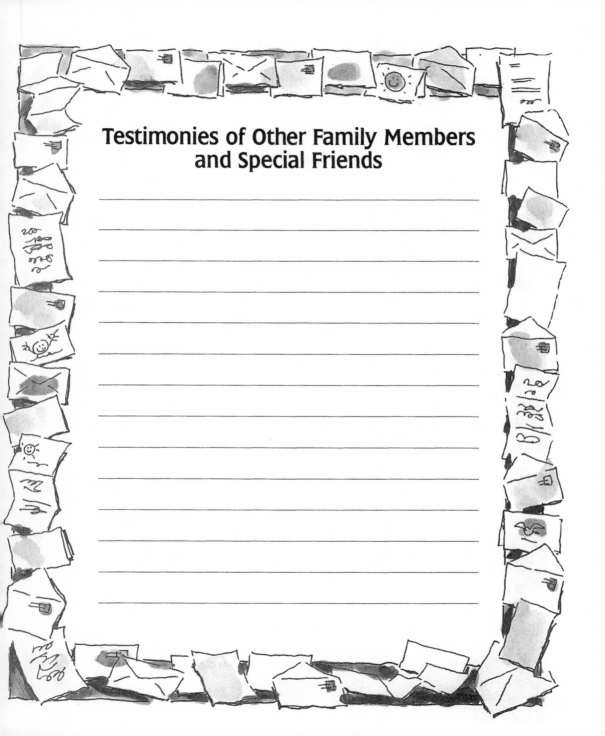

Testimonies of Other Family Members and Special Friends

_____

_____

_____

_____

_____

_____

_____

_____

_____

_____

_____

_____

_____

_____

_____

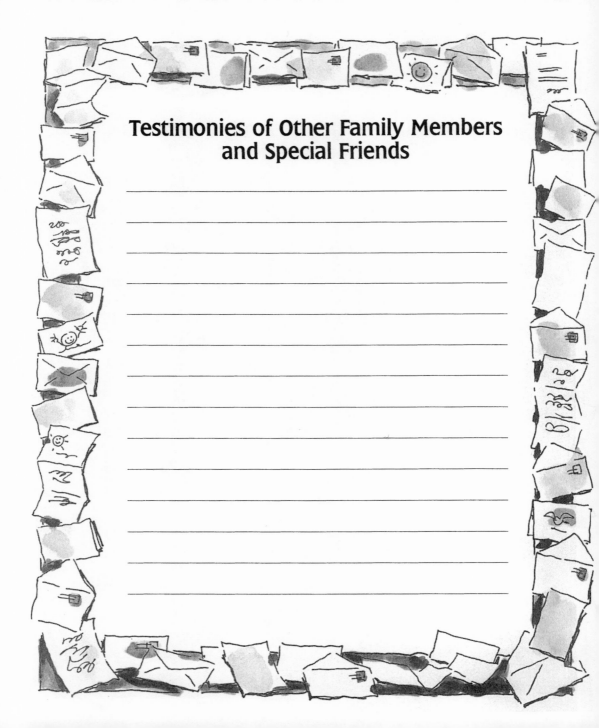

Testimonies of Other Family Members and Special Friends

Testimonies of Other Family Members and Special Friends

_____

_____

_____

_____

_____

_____

_____

_____

_____

_____

_____

_____

_____

_____

Testimonies of Other Family Members and Special Friends

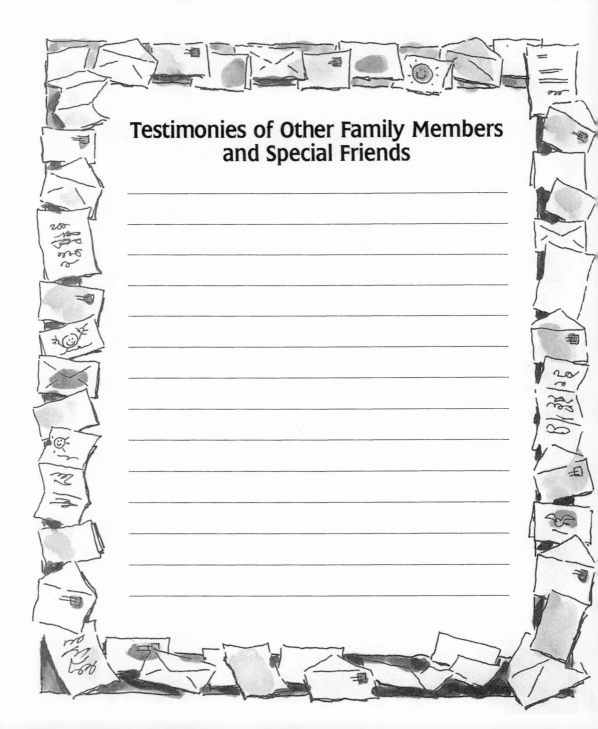

Testimonies of Other Family Members and Special Friends

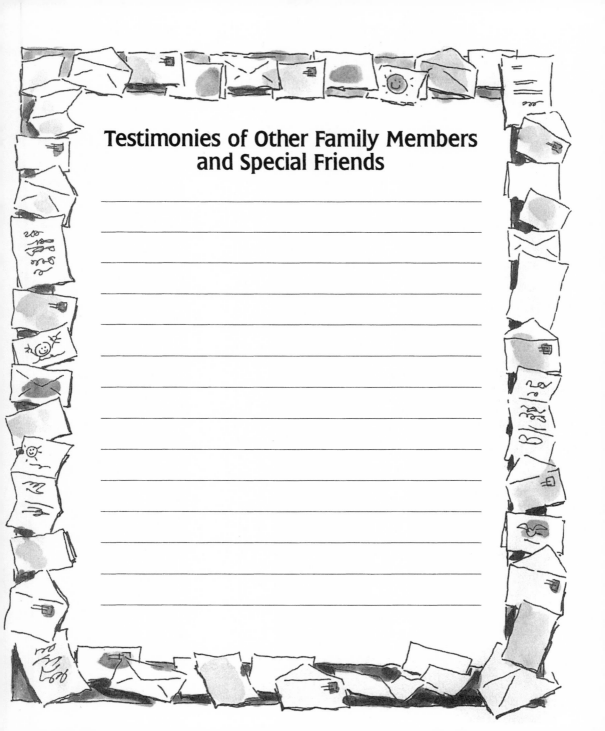

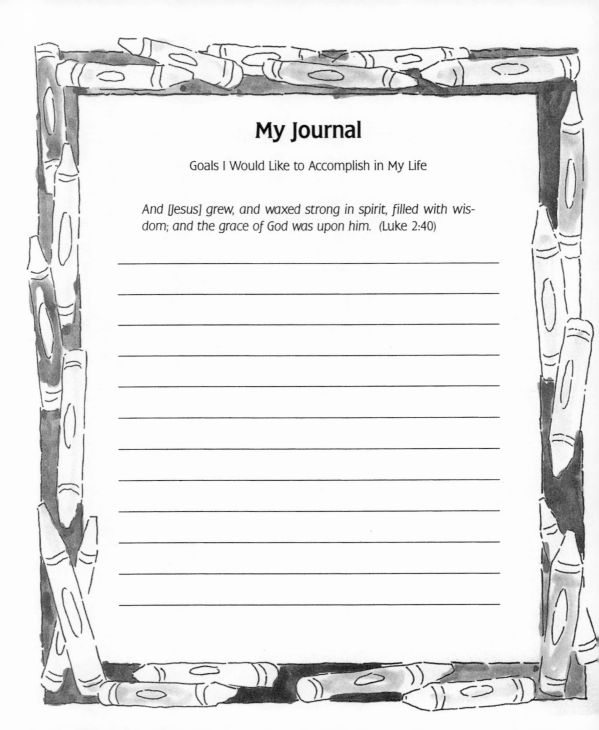

My Journal

Goals I Would Like to Accomplish in My Life

And [Jesus] grew, and waxed strong in spirit, filled with wisdom; and the grace of God was upon him. (Luke 2:40)

_____

_____

_____

_____

_____

_____

_____

_____

_____

_____

_____

My Journal

Date _____

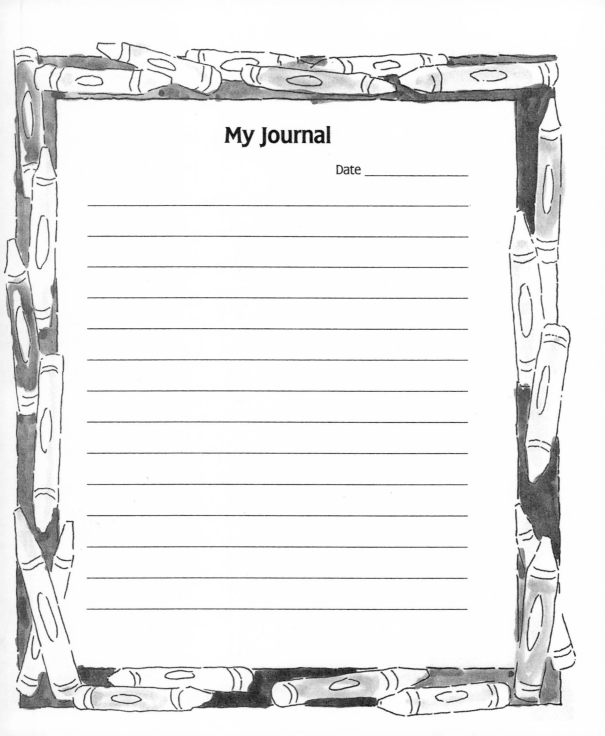

_____

_____

_____

_____

_____

_____

_____

_____

_____

_____

_____

_____

_____

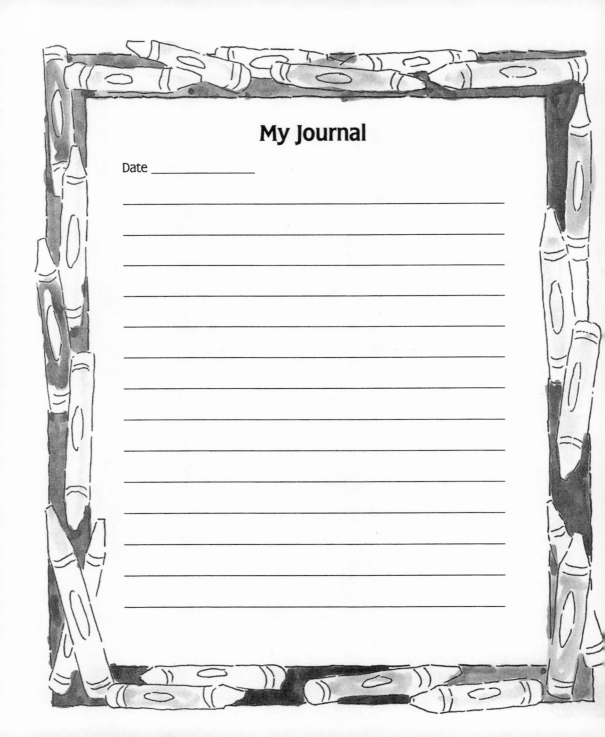

My Journal

Date _____

_____

_____

_____

_____

_____

_____

_____

_____

_____

_____

_____

_____

_____

_____

_____

My Journal

Date _____

_____

_____

_____

_____

_____

_____

_____

_____

_____

_____

_____

_____

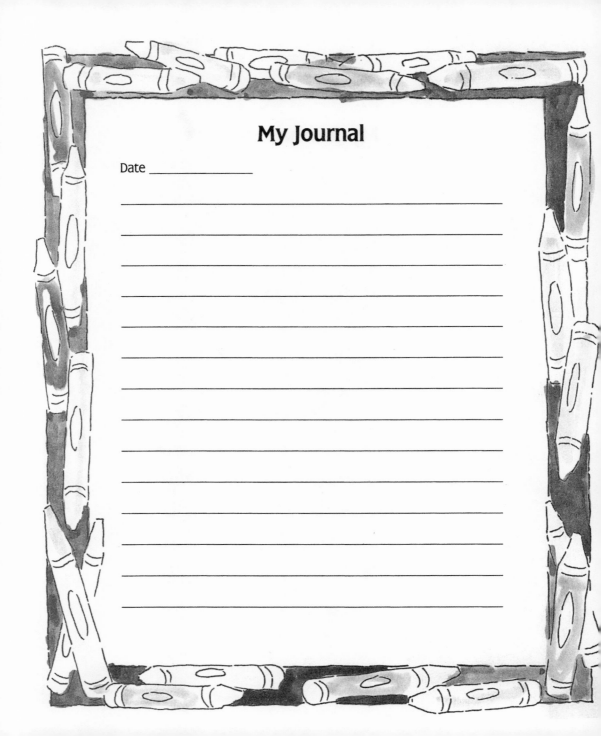

My Journal

Date _____

_____

_____

_____

_____

_____

_____

_____

_____

_____

_____

_____

_____

_____

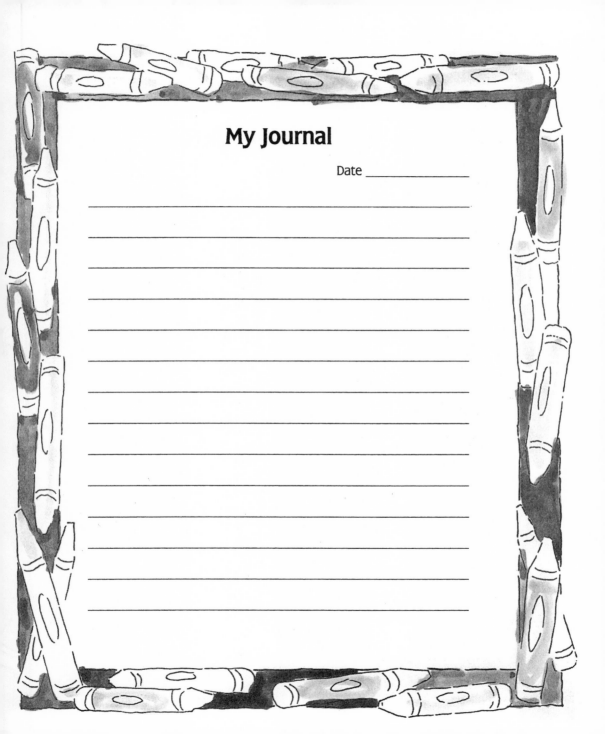

My Journal

Date _____

_____

_____

_____

_____

_____

_____

_____

_____

_____

_____

_____

_____

_____

_____

_____

My Journal

Date _____

_____

_____

_____

_____

_____

_____

_____

_____

_____

_____

_____

_____

_____

_____

_____

_____

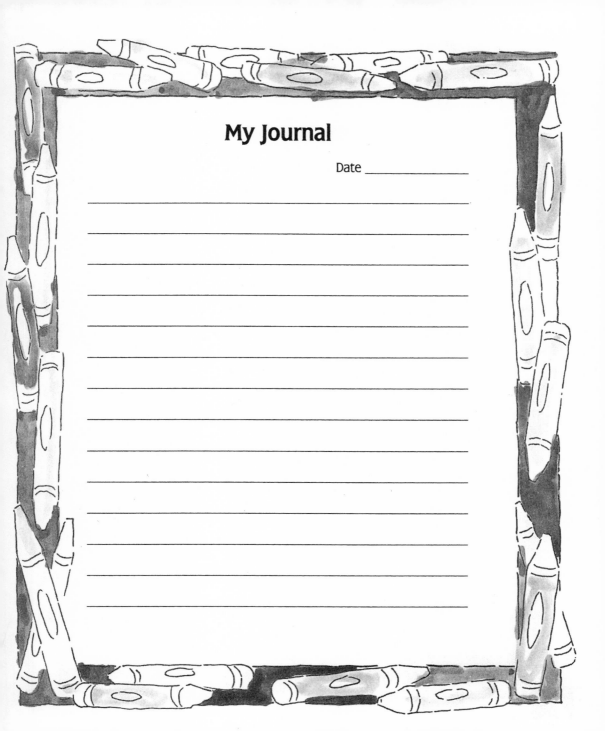

My Journal

Date _____

_____

_____

_____

_____

_____

_____

_____

_____

_____

_____

_____

_____

_____

My Journal

Date _____

_____

_____

_____

_____

_____

_____

_____

_____

_____

_____

_____

_____

_____

_____

My Journal

Date _____

_____

_____

_____

_____

_____

_____

_____

_____

_____

_____

_____

_____

_____

_____

_____

_____

My Journal

Date _____

_____

_____

_____

_____

_____

_____

_____

_____

_____

_____

_____

_____

_____

_____

_____

_____

My Journal

Date _____

_____

_____

_____

_____

_____

_____

_____

_____

_____

_____

_____

_____

_____

_____

My Journal

Date _____

_____

_____

_____

_____

_____

_____

_____

_____

_____

_____

_____

_____

_____

_____

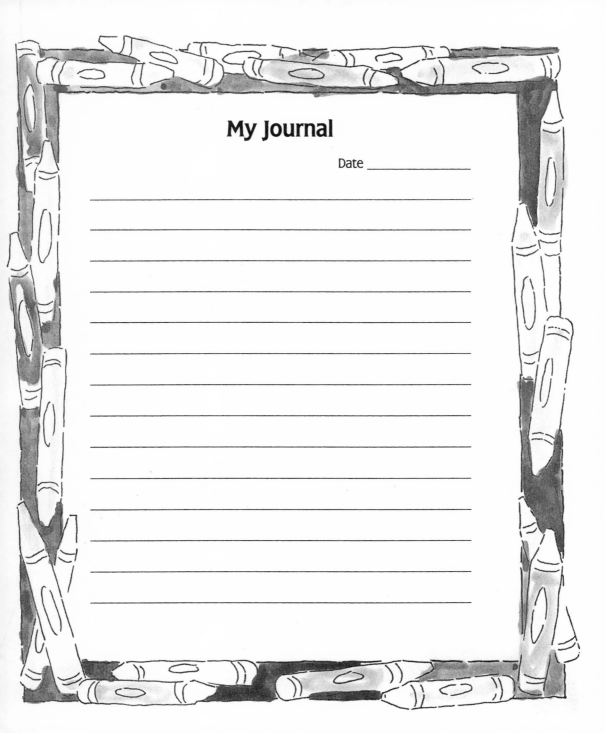

My Journal

Date _____

_____

_____

_____

_____

_____

_____

_____

_____

_____

_____

_____

_____

_____

My Journal

Date _____

_____

_____

_____

_____

_____

_____

_____

_____

_____

_____

_____

_____

_____

_____

_____

_____

My Journal

Date _____

_____

_____

_____

_____

_____

_____

_____

_____

_____

_____

_____

_____

_____

_____

My Journal

Date _____

_____

_____

_____

_____

_____

_____

_____

_____

_____

_____

_____

_____

_____

_____

_____

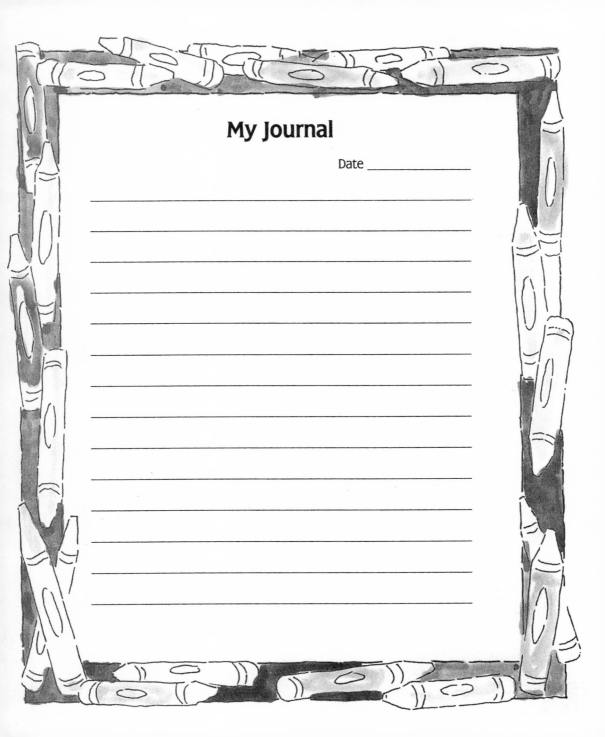

My Journal

Date _____

_____

_____

_____

_____

_____

_____

_____

_____

_____

_____

_____

_____

_____

_____

_____

_____

_____

_____

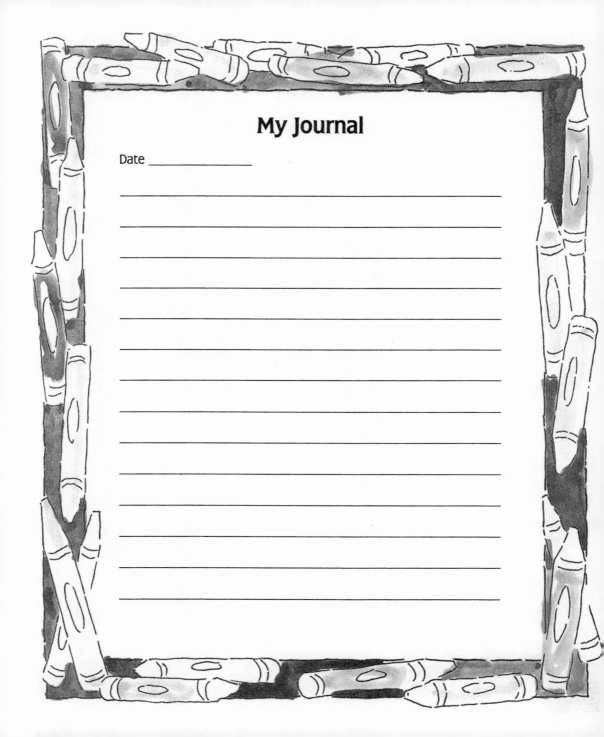

My Journal

Date _____

_____

_____

_____

_____

_____

_____

_____

_____

_____

_____

_____

_____

_____

_____

_____

_____

My Journal

Date _____

_____

_____

_____

_____

_____

_____

_____

_____

_____

_____

_____

_____

_____

_____

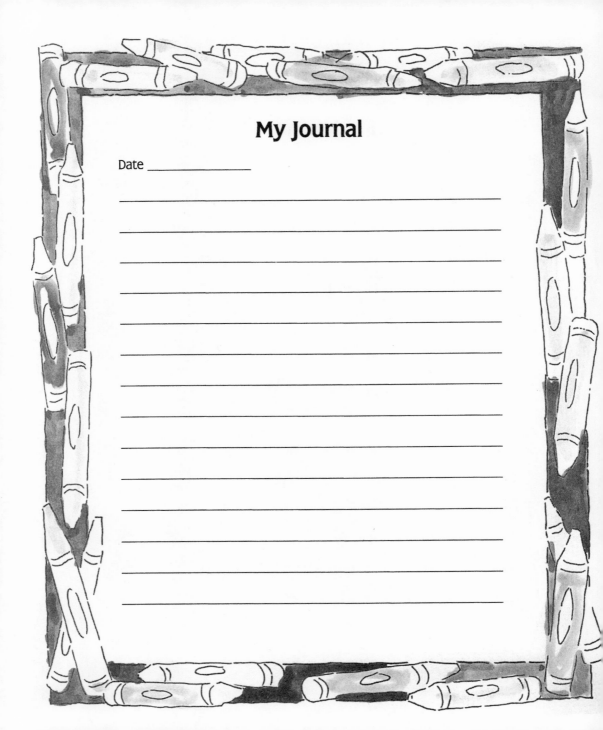

My Journal

Date _____

_____

_____

_____

_____

_____

_____

_____

_____

_____

_____

_____

_____

_____

_____

My Journal

Date _____

_____

_____

_____

_____

_____

_____

_____

_____

_____

_____

_____

_____

_____

My Journal

Date _____

_____

_____

_____

_____

_____

_____

_____

_____

_____

_____

_____

_____

_____

_____

_____

My Journal

Date _____

_____

_____

_____

_____

_____

_____

_____

_____

_____

_____

_____

_____

_____

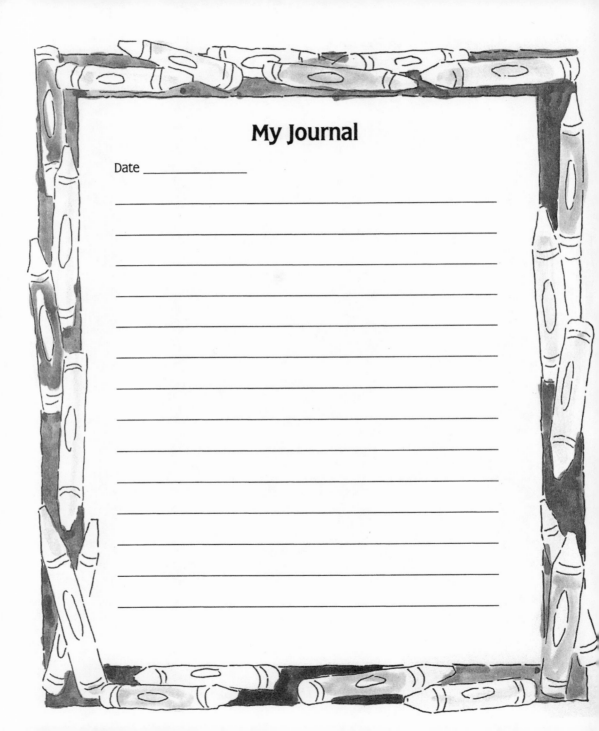

My Journal

Date _____

_____

_____

_____

_____

_____

_____

_____

_____

_____

_____

_____

_____

_____

_____

_____

My Journal

Date _____

_____
_____
_____
_____
_____
_____
_____
_____
_____
_____
_____
_____
_____
_____
_____
_____

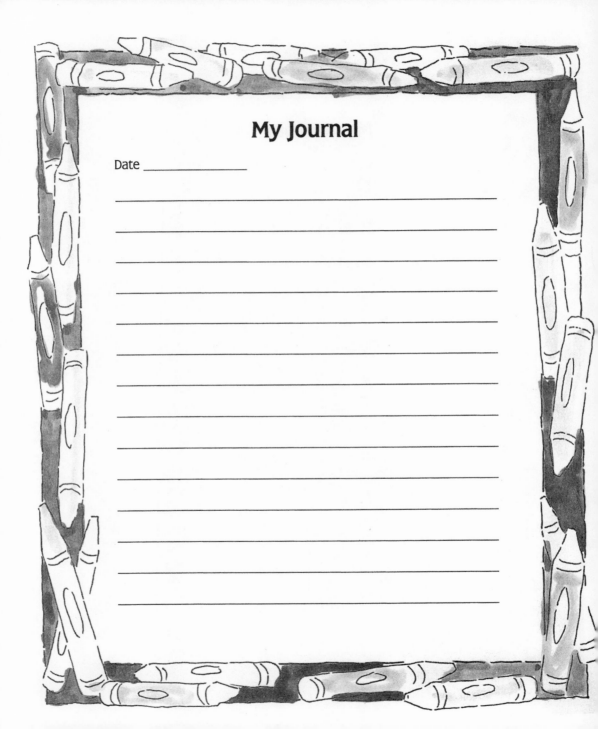

My Journal

Date _____

_____

_____

_____

_____

_____

_____

_____

_____

_____

_____

_____

_____

_____

_____

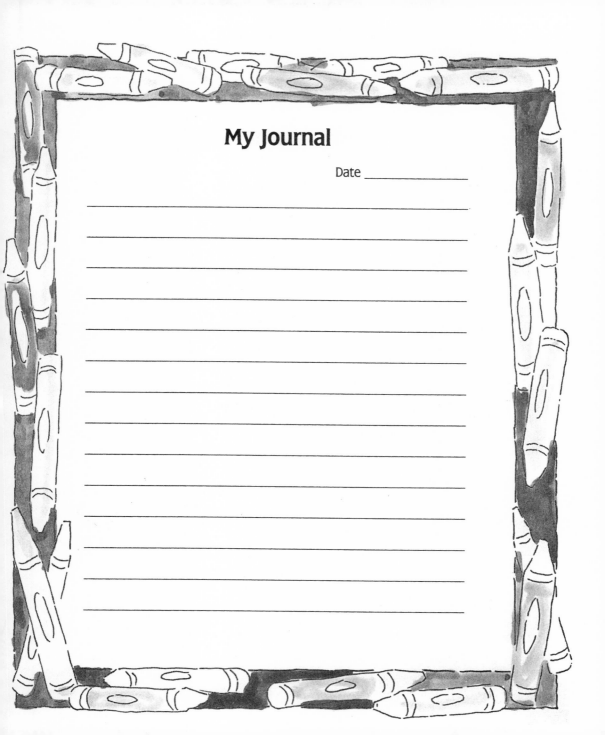

My Journal

Date _____

_____

_____

_____

_____

_____

_____

_____

_____

_____

_____

_____

_____

_____

_____

_____

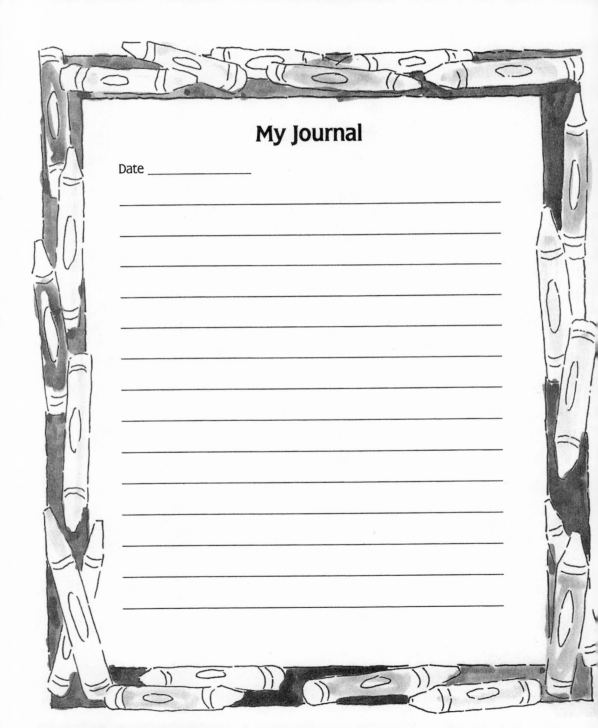

My Journal

Date _____

_____

_____

_____

_____

_____

_____

_____

_____

_____

_____

_____

_____

_____

_____

_____

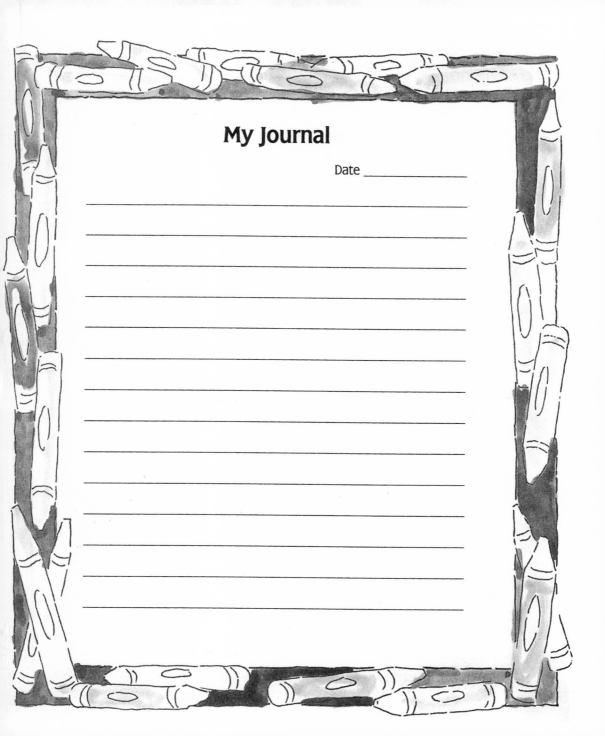

My Journal

Date _____

_____

_____

_____

_____

_____

_____

_____

_____

_____

_____

_____

_____

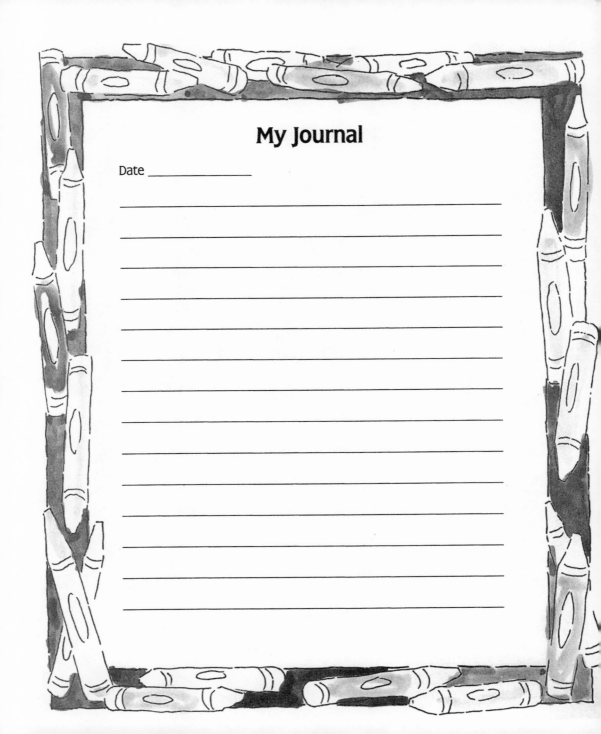

My Journal

Date _____

_____

_____

_____

_____

_____

_____

_____

_____

_____

_____

_____

_____

_____

_____

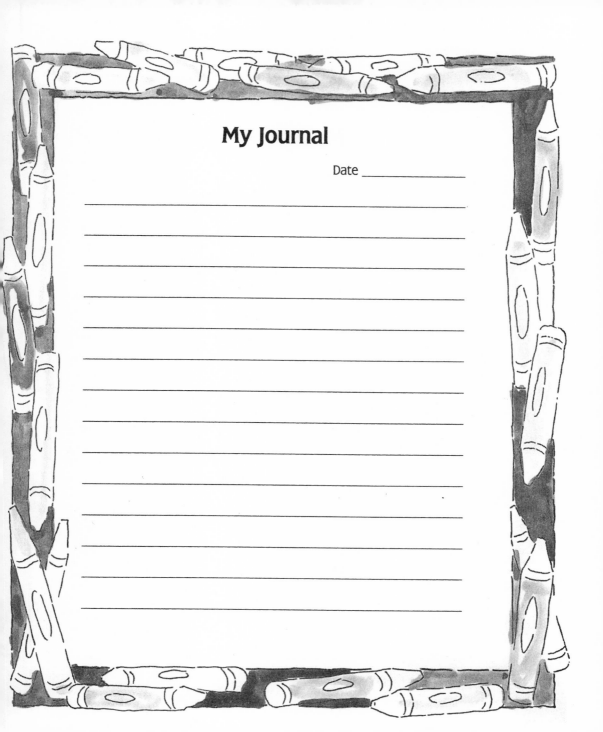

My Journal

Date _____

_____

_____

_____

_____

_____

_____

_____

_____

_____

_____

_____

_____

_____

_____

My Journal

Date _____

_____

_____

_____

_____

_____

_____

_____

_____

_____

_____

_____

_____

_____

_____

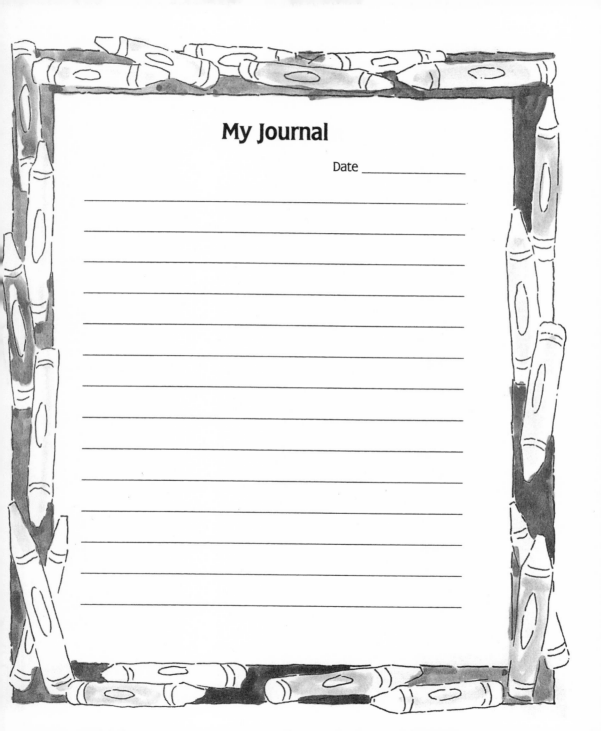

My Journal

Date _____

_____

_____

_____

_____

_____

_____

_____

_____

_____

_____

_____

_____

_____

_____

_____

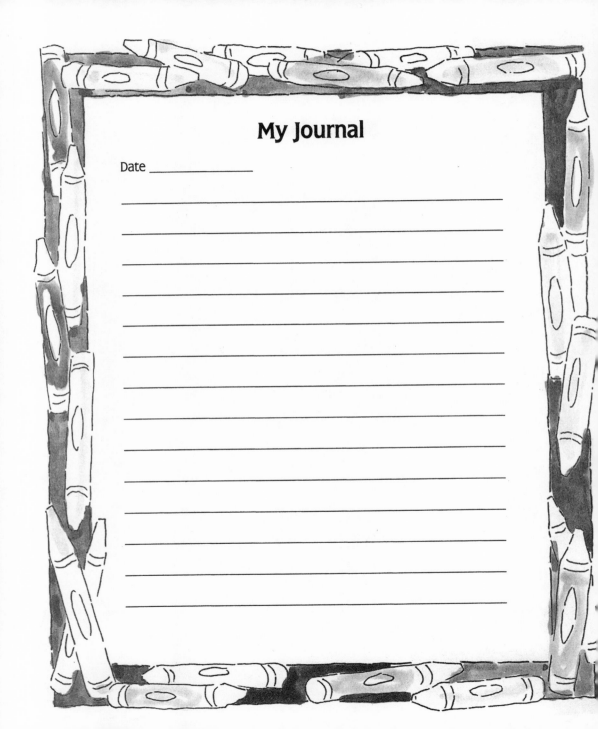

My Journal

Date _____

_____

_____

_____

_____

_____

_____

_____

_____

_____

_____

_____

_____

_____

_____